45p

THE RHYMING RIVER

I

POETRY BOOKS BY JAMES REEVES

ANTHOLOGIES

Heinemann's Junior Poetry Books: a collection of rhymes and poems
for use in Primary Schools
1 *Yellow Wheels*
2 *Grey Goose and Gander*
3 *Green Broom*
4 *Strawberry Fair*
The Merry-Go-Round (the above four books in one volume)
The Rhyming River: an anthology of poetry for secondary schools
Book One (illustrated by Peter Dunbar)
Book Two (illustrated by Jane Paton)
Book Three (illustrated by Robert Hodgson)
Book Four (illustrated by Peggy Fortnum)
Orpheus Book I (English poetry for 10–12-year-olds)
Orpheus Book II (English poetry for 13–15-year-olds)
The Poets' World (an anthology of English poetry)
The Speaking Oak (a miscellany of English prose and poetry)

POEMS FOR CHILDREN

Hurdy Gurdy
The Wandering Moon
Prefabulous Animiles with Edward Ardizzone

THE POETRY BOOKSHELF SERIES

Selections with introductions and notes
D. H. Lawrence
John Donne
Gerard Manley Hopkins
John Clare
Robert Browning
Samuel Taylor Coleridge
Emily Dickinson
The Modern Poets' World

LITERARY CRITICISM

A Short History of English Poetry

FOR TEACHERS

Teaching Poetry: Poetry in Class, Five to Fifteen

THE RHYMING RIVER

BOOK ONE

an anthology of verse chosen by
JAMES REEVES

with illustrations by
PETER DUNBAR
and from contemporary sources

HEINEMANN EDUCATIONAL
BOOKS LTD · LONDON

Heinemann Educational Books Ltd
LONDON   MELBOURNE   TORONTO
SINGAPORE   AUCKLAND
IBADAN   CAPE TOWN
HONG KONG

First published 1959
Reprinted 1960, 1966

Published by
Heinemann Educational Books Ltd
48 Charles Street, London W.1
Printed in Great Britain by
Butler & Tanner Ltd
Frome and London

CONTENTS

I

II

III

IV

VIII

ACKNOWLEDGEMENTS

THE EDITOR and publishers wish to thank the following for their permission to include copyright material in this anthology: Messrs Jonathan Cape for 'Goldenhair' from *Chamber Music* by James Joyce, and for 'My Garden' and 'Sheep' from *Collected Poems of W. H. Davies*; Messrs Gerald Duckworth & Co Ltd for 'The Hippopotamus', 'Jim' (with the illustrations) and 'The Big Baboon' from *Cautionary Verses* by Hilaire Belloc; the Literary Trustees of the late Walter de la Mare and Messrs Faber & Faber for nine poems by Walter de la Mare; the executors of Miss Mary Coleridge for 'The Deserted House' and 'Veneta' from *Collected Poems of Mary Coleridge* published by Messrs Rupert Hart-Davis; and the Oxford University Press for a poem from *The Blackbird in the Lilac* by James Reeves. The text of the Authorized Version of the Bible and the Book of Common Prayer are Crown copyright, and the extracts used are reproduced by permission. Thanks are also due to the Trustees of the British Museum for the illustrations on pages 54, 71, 87, 99 and 100, to the Trustees of the National Portrait Gallery for those on pages 7 and 43, to the Trustees of the National Maritime Museum, Greenwich, for the portrait on p. 73, and to the Mansell Collection for the illustrations on pages 26, 60, and 112-13.

Spring

SPRING, the sweet Spring, is the year's pleasant king:
Then blooms each thing; then maids dance in a ring;
Cold doth not sting; the pretty birds do sing,
  Cuckoo, jug-jug, pu-we, to-witta-woo!

The palm and may make country houses gay;
Lambs frisk and play; the shepherds pipe all day;
And we hear aye birds tune this merry lay,
  Cuckoo, jug-jug, pu-we, to-witta-woo!

The fields breathe sweet; the daisies kiss our feet;
Young lovers meet; old wives a-sunning sit;
In every street these tunes our ears do greet,
  Cuckoo, jug-jug, pu-we, to-witta-woo!
    Spring, the sweet Spring!

THOMAS NASH

Clock-a-Clay

In the cowslip pips I lie,
Hidden from the buzzing fly,
While green grass beneath me lies,
Pearled with dew like fishes' eyes,
Here I lie, a clock-a-clay,[1]
Waiting for the time of day.

While the forest quakes surprise,
And the wild wind sobs and sighs,
My home ricks are like to fall,
On its pillar green and tall;
When the pattering rain drives by
Clock-a-clay keeps warm and dry.

Day by day and night by night,
All the week I hide from sight;
In the cowslip pips I lie,
In rain and dew still warm and dry;
Day and night, and night and day,
Red, black-spotted clock-a-clay.

My home shakes in wind and showers,
Pale green pillar topped with flowers,
Bending at the wild wind's breath,
Till I touch the grass beneath,
Here I live, lone clock-a-clay,
Watching for the time of day.

JOHN CLARE

[1] Ladybird.

Written in March

THE Cock is crowing.
The stream is flowing
The small birds twitter
The lake doth glitter,
The green field sleeps in the sun;
The oldest and youngest
Are at work with the strongest;
The cattle are grazing,
Their heads never raising;
There are forty feeding like one!

Like an army defeated
The snow hath retreated,
And now doth fare ill
On the top of the bare hill;
The Ploughboy is whooping-anon-anon:
There's joy in the mountains;
There's life in the fountains;
Small clouds are sailing,
Blue sky prevailing;
The rain is over and gone!

WILLIAM WORDSWORTH

The Deserted House

THERE'S no smoke in the chimney,
  And the rain beats on the floor;
There's no glass in the window,
  There's no wood in the door;
The heather grows behind the house,
  And the sand lies before.

No hand hath trained the ivy,
  The walls are grey and bare;
The boats upon the sea sail by,
  Nor ever tarry there.
No beast of the field comes nigh,
  Nor any bird of the air.

MARY COLERIDGE

The Old Stone House

NOTHING on the grey roof, nothing on the brown,
Only a little greening where the rain drips down;
Nobody at the window, nobody at the door,
Only a little hollow which a foot once wore;
But still I tread on tiptoe, still tiptoe on I go,
Past nettles, porch, and weedy well, for oh, I know
A friendless face is peering, and a still clear eye
Peeps closely through the casement as my step
    goes by.

WALTER DE LA MARE

The Snail

AT sunset, when the night-dews fall,
Out of the ivy on the wall
With horns outstretched and pointed tail
Comes the grey and noiseless snail.
On ivy stems she clambers down,
Carrying her house of brown.
Safe in the dark, no greedy eye
Can her tender body spy,
While she herself, a hungry thief,
Searches out the freshest leaf.
She travels on as best she can
Like a toppling caravan.

JAMES REEVES

From a Railway Carriage

FASTER than fairies, faster than witches,
Bridges and houses, hedges and ditches,
And charging along like troops in a battle,
All through the meadows the horses and cattle:
All of the sights of the hill and the plain
Fly as thick as driving rain;
And ever again, in the wink of an eye,
Painted stations whistle by.

Here is a child who clambers and scrambles,
All by himself and gathering brambles;
Here is a tramp who stands and gazes;
And there is the green for stringing the daisies!
Here is a cart run away in the road,
Lumping along with man and load;
And here is a mill, and there is a river;
Each a glimpse and gone for ever!

ROBERT LOUIS STEVENSON

ROBERT LOUIS STEVENSON
from a painting by W. B. Richmond (1887)

When Icicles Hang by the Wall

WHEN icicles hang by the wall,
  And Dick the shepherd blows his nail;
When Tom bears logs into the hall,
  And milk comes frozen home in pail;
When blood is nipped, and ways be foul,
—Then nightly sings the staring owl:
  To-who,
To-whit, To-who—a merry note,
While greasy Joan doth keel[1] the pot.

When all aloud the wind doth blow,
  And coughing drowns the parson's saw,
And birds sit brooding in the snow,
  And Marian's nose looks red and raw;
When roasted crabs[2] hiss in the bowl,
—Then nightly sings the staring owl:
  To-who,
To-whit, To-who—a merry note,
While greasy Joan doth keel the pot.

WILLIAM SHAKESPEARE

[1] Keep from boiling over.   [2] Crabapples.

The Birds

HE   Where thou dwellest, in what grove,
Tell me, fair one, tell me, love;
Where thou thy charming nest dost build,
O thou pride of every field!

SHE   Yonder stands a lonely tree,
There I live and mourn for thee.
Morning drinks my silent tear,
And evening winds my sorrow bear.

HE   O thou summer's harmony,
I have lived and mourned for thee.
Each day I mourn along the wood,
And night hath heard my sorrows loud.

SHE   Dost thou truly long for me?
And am I thus sweet to thee?
Sorrow now is at an end,
O my lover and my friend!

HE   Come, on wings of joy we'll fly
To where my bower hangs on high!
Come, and make thy calm retreat
Among green leaves and blossoms sweet!

WILLIAM BLAKE

Veneta

WIND and waters ring the bells
   That rang for them of high degree
Trumpets are the sounding shells
   In the city under the sea.

Where a queen was wont to hide
   Her outwearied majesty,
Swim the fishes open-eyed
   In the city under the sea.

Many a street lies broad and fair,
   Many a palace fair and free,
Neither a man nor woman there,
   In the city under the sea.

MARY COLERIDGE

No Jewel

No jewel from the rock
Is lovely as the dew,
Flashing with flamelike red
With sea-like blue.

No web the merchant weaves
Can rival hers—
The silk the spider spins
Across the furze.

WALTER DE LA MARE

10

Little Trotty Wagtail

LITTLE trotty wagtail, he went in the rain,
And tittering, tottering sideways he ne'er got straight again,
He stooped to get a worm, and looked up to catch a fly,
And then he flew away ere his feathers they were dry.

Little trotty wagtail, he waddled in the mud,
And left his little footmarks, trample where he would.
And waddled in the water-pudge, and waggle went his tail,
And chirrup up his wings to dry upon the garden rail.

Little trotty wagtail, you nimble all about,
And in the dimpling water-pudge you waddle in and out;
Your home is nigh at hand, and in the warm pigsty,
So, little Master Wagtail, I'll bid you a good-bye.

JOHN CLARE

WAGTAIL
wood engraving by Thomas Bewick (about 1800)

11

Nicholas Nye

THISTLE and darnel and dock grew there,
 And a bush, in the corner, of may,
On the orchard wall I used to sprawl
 In the blazing heat of the day;
Half asleep and half awake,
 While the birds went twittering by,
And nobody there my lone to share
 But Nicholas Nye.

Nicholas Nye was lean and grey,
 Lame of a leg and old,
More than a score of donkey's years
 He had seen since he was foaled;
He munched the thistles, purple and spiked,
 Would sometimes stoop and sigh,
And turn his head, as if he said,
 'Poor Nicholas Nye!'

Alone with his shadow he'd drowse in the meadow,
　Lazily swinging his tail,
At break of day he used to bray,—
　Not much too hearty and hale;
But a wonderful gumption was under his skin,
　And a clear calm light in his eye;
And once in a while—he'd smile . . .
　　Would Nicholas Nye.

Seem to be smiling at me, he would,
　From his bush in the corner, of may,—
Bony and ownerless, widowed and worn,
　Knobble-kneed, lonely and grey;
And over the grass would seem to pass,
　'Neath the deep dark blue of the sky,
Something much better than words between me
　　And Nicholas Nye.

But dusk would come in the apple boughs,
　The green of the glow-worm shine,
The birds in nest would crouch to rest,
　And home I'd trudge to mine;
And there, in the moonlight, dark with dew,
　Asking not wherefore nor why,
Would brood like a ghost, and as still as a post,
　　Old Nicholas Nye.

WALTER DE LA MARE

Silver

SLOWLY, silently, now the moon
Walks the night in her silver shoon;
This way, and that, she peers, and sees
Silver fruit upon silver trees;
One by one the casements catch
Her beams beneath the silvery thatch;
Couched in his kennel, like a log,
With paws of silver sleeps the dog;
From their shadowy cote the white breasts peep
Of doves in a silver-feathered sleep;
A harvest mouse goes scampering by,
With silver claws, and silver eye;
And moveless fish in the water gleam,
By silver reeds in a silver stream.

WALTER DE LA MARE

14

Old Shellover

'COME!' said Old Shellover.
'What?' says Creep.
'The horny old Gardener's fast asleep;
The fat cock Thrush
To his nest has gone,
And the dew shines bright
In the rising Moon;
Old Sallie Worm from her hole doth peep;
'Come!' said Old Shellover.
'Ay!' said Creep.

WALTER DE LA MARE

Sweet Suffolk Owl

SWEET Suffolk owl, so trimly dight[1]
With feathers like a lady bright,
Thou sing'st alone, sitting by night,
    Tu-whit, tu-whoo!

Thy note, that forth so freely rolls,
With shrill command the mouse controls,
And sings a dirge for dying souls,
    Tu-whit, tu-whoo!

THOMAS VAUTOR

[1] Dressed.

The Owl

WHEN cats run home and light is come,
　And dew is cold upon the ground,
And the far-off stream is dumb,
　And the whirring sail goes round,
　And the whirring sail goes round;
　　Alone and warming his five wits,
　　The white owl in the belfry sits.

When merry milkmaids click the latch,
　And rarely smells the new-mown hay,
And the cock hath sung beneath the thatch
　Twice or thrice his roundelay,
　Twice or thrice his roundelay;
　　Alone and warming his five wits,
　　The white owl in the belfry sits.

ALFRED TENNYSON

The Flint

AN emerald is as green as grass,
　A ruby red as blood,
A sapphire shines as blue as heaven;
　But a flint lies in the mud.
A diamond is a brilliant stone
　To catch the world's desire;
An opal holds a rainbow light,
　But a flint holds fire.

CHRISTINA ROSSETTI

II

As I Sat on a Sunny Bank

As I sat on a sunny bank,
On Christmas Day in the morning,

I spied three ships come sailing by,
On Christmas Day in the morning.

And who should be with those three ships
But Joseph and his fair lady!

O he did whistle, and she did sing,
On Christmas Day in the morning.

And all the bells on earth did ring,
On Christmas Day in the morning.

For joy that our Saviour he was born
On Christmas Day in the morning.

TRADITIONAL

17

The Foolish Boy

My father died, and I cannot tell how,
He left me six horses to follow the plough.
With a wing-wang-waddle, oh!
Jack sold his saddle, oh!
Blossy boys, bubble oh! under the broom.

I sold my six horses and bought me a cow,
I'd fain have a fortune, but didn't know how.
With a wing-wang-waddle, oh! . . .

I sold me a cow and bought me a calf,
I'd fain have a fortune, but I lost a half.
With a wing-wang-waddle, oh! . . .

I sold my calf and bought me a cat;
The pretty thing by my chimney sat.
With a wing-wang-waddle, oh! . . .

I sold my cat and I bought me a mouse;
He fired his tail and he burnt down my house.
With a wing-wang-waddle, oh! . . .

I have nothing to buy and I've nothing to sell,
And how I shall live, I'm sure I can't tell.
With a wing-wang-waddle, oh! . . .

TRADITIONAL

The Smuggler

O MY true love's a smuggler and sails upon the sea,
And I would I were a seaman to go along with he;
To go along with he for the satins and the wine,
And run the tubs at Slapton when the stars do shine.

O Hollands is a good drink when the nights are cold,
And Brandy is a good drink for them as grows old.
There is lights in the cliff-top when the boats are home-bound,
And we run the tubs at Slapton when the word goes round.

The King he is a proud man in his grand red coat,
But I do love a smuggler in a little fishing-boat;
For he runs the Mallins lace and he spends his money free,
And I would I were a seaman to go along with he.

Brennan on the Moor

IT's of a fearless highwayman a story I will tell;
His name was William Brennan and in Ireland he did dwell.
Upon the Libbery Mountains he commenced his wild career,
Where many a wealthy gentleman before him shook with fear.
   Brennan on the moor! Brennan on the moor!
   Bold and undaunted stood Brennan on the moor!

One day he robbed a packman and his name was Pedlar Bawn;
They travelled on together till the day began to dawn;
The pedlar found his money gone, likewise his watch and chain,
He at once encountered Brennan, and he robbed him back again.
   Brennan on the moor! . . .

When Brennan saw the pedlar was as good a man as he,
He took him on the highway his companion to be;
The pedlar threw away his pack without any delay,
And proved a faithful comrade until his dying day.
   Brennan on the moor! . . .

20

One day upon the King's highway as Willie he sat down,
He met the Mayor of Cashel just a mile outside the town;
The Mayor he knew his features: 'Oh, you're my man!' said he,
'I think you're William Brennan—you must come along with
    me!'
   Brennan on the moor! . . .

Now Willie's wife had been to town provisions for to buy,
And when she saw her Willie she began to sob and cry;
He said, 'Give me that tenpence[1]!' and as quick as Willie spoke,
She handed him a blunderbuss from underneath her cloak.
   Brennan on the moor! . . .

Now with this loaded blunderbuss, the truth I will unfold,
He made the Mayor to tremble, and he robbed him of his gold;
A hundred pounds was offered for his apprehension there,
But he with horse and saddle to the mountains did repair.
   Brennan on the moor! . . .

He lay among the fern all day, 'twas thick upon the field,
And many wounds he did receive before that he would yield;
He was captured and found guilty, and the Judge made this reply:
'For robbing on the King's highway you are condemned to die!'
   Brennan on the moor! . . .

TRADITIONAL

[1] Thieves' slang for a gun.

The Three Jovial Welshmen

THERE were three jovial Welshmen,
 As I have heard them say,
And they would go a-hunting
 Upon St David's day.

All the day they hunted,
 And nothing could they find
But a ship a-sailing,
 A-sailing with the wind.

One said it was a ship;
 The other he said nay;
The third said it was a house
 With the chimney blown away.

And all the night they hunted,
 And nothing could they find
But the moon a-gliding,
 A-gliding with the wind.

One said it was the moon;
 The other he said nay;
The third said it was a cheese
 And half of it cut away.

And all the day they hunted,
 And nothing could they find
But a hedgehog in a bramble-bush,
 And that they left behind.

The first said it was a hedgehog;
    The second he said nay;
The third it was a pincushion,
    And the pins stuck in wrong way.

And all the night they hunted,
    And nothing could they find
But a hare in a turnip field,
    And that they left behind.

The first said it was a hare;
    The second he said nay;
The third said it was a calf
    And the cow had run away.

And all the day they hunted,
    And nothing could they find
But an owl in a holly-tree,
    And that they left behind.

One said it was an owl;
    The other he said nay;
The third it was an old man,
    And his beard a-growing grey.

There were three jovial Welshmen,
    As I have heard them say.
And they would go a-hunting
    Upon St David's day.

TRADITIONAL

Elsie Marley

Do you ken Elsie Marley, honey?
The wife that sells the barley, honey?
She lost her pocket and all her money
At the back o' the bush in the garden, honey.
Do you ken Elsie Marley, honey?

Elsie Marley's grown so fine
She won't get up to feed the swine,
But lies in bed till eight or nine,
And surely she does take her time.
Do you ken Elsie Marley, honey?

Elsie Marley wore a straw hat,
But now she's gotten a velvet cap,
—The Lambton lads must pay for that.
Do you ken Elsie Marley, honey?

TRADITIONAL

The Fairies

IF ye will with Mab find grace,
Set each platter in his place:
Rake the fire up, and get
Water in, ere sun be set.
Wash your pails, and cleanse your dairies;
Sluts are loathsome to the fairies:
Sweep your house: who doth not so,
Mab will pinch her by the toe.

ROBERT HERRICK

Poor Old Horse

My clothing was once of the linsey woolsey fine,
My tail it grew at length, my coat did likewise shine;
But now I'm growing old; my beauty does decay,
My master frowns upon me; one day I heard him say,
     Poor old horse: poor old horse.

Once I was kept in the stable snug and warm,
To keep my tender limbs from any cold or harm;
But now, in open fields, I am forced for to go,
In all sorts of weather, let it be hail, rain, freeze, or snow.
     Poor old horse: poor old horse.

Once I was fed on the very best corn and hay
That ever grew in yon fields, or in yon meadows gay;
But now there's no such doing can I find at all,
I'm glad to pick the green sprouts that grow behind yon wall.
     Poor old horse: poor old horse.

'You are old, you are cold, you are deaf, dull, dumb and slow,
You are not fit for anything, or in my team to draw.
You have eaten all my hay, you have spoiled all my straw,
So hang him, whip, stick him, to the huntsman let him go.'
     Poor old horse: poor old horse.

My hide unto the tanners then I would freely give,
My body to the hound dogs, I would rather die than live,
Likewise my poor old bones that have carried you many a mile,
Over hedges, ditches, brooks, bridges, likewise gates and stiles.
     Poor old horse: poor old horse.

TRADITIONAL

Meg Merrilies

OLD Meg she was a gipsy,
  And lived upon the moors:
Her bed it was the brown heath turf,
  And her house was out of doors.
Her apples were swart blackberries,
  Her currants, pods o' broom;
Her wine was dew of the wild white rose,
  Her book a churchyard tomb.

Her brothers were the craggy hills,
    Her sisters larchen trees;
Alone with her great family
    She lived as she did please.
No breakfast had she many a morn,
    No dinner many a noon,
And, 'stead of supper, she would stare
    Full hard against the moon.

And every morn of woodbine fresh
    She made her garlanding,
And every night the dark glen yew
    She wove, and she would sing.
And with her fingers old and brown
    She plaited mats o' rushes,
And gave them to the cottagers
    She met among the bushes.

Old Meg was brave as Margaret Queen
    And tall as Amazon;
An old red blanket cloak she wore;
    A chip hat had she on.
God rest her aged bones somewhere—
    She died full long agone!

                              JOHN KEATS

The Holly and the Ivy

THE holly and the ivy,
When they are both full grown,
Of all the trees that are in the wood,
The holly bears the crown:
> *The rising of the sun*
> *And the running of the deer,*
> *The playing of the merry organ,*
> *Sweet singing in the choir.*

The holly bears a blossom,
As white as the lily flower,
And Mary bore sweet Jesus Christ,
To be our sweet Saviour:

The holly bears a berry,
As red as any blood,
And Mary bore sweet Jesus Christ,
To do poor sinners good:

The holly bears a prickle,
As sharp as any thorn,
And Mary bore sweet Jesus Christ,
On Christmas day in the morn:

The holly bears a bark,
As bitter as any gall,
And Mary bore sweet Jesus Christ,
For to redeem us all:

The holly and the ivy,
When they are both full grown,
Of all the trees that are in the wood,
The holly bears the crown.

TRADITIONAL

The Old Soldier

THERE came an Old Soldier to my door,
Asked a crust, and asked no more;
The wars had thinned him very bare,
Fighting and marching everywhere,
  With a Fol rol dol rol di do.

With nose stuck out, and cheek sunk in,
A bristling beard upon his chin—
Powder and bullets and wounds and drums
Had come to that Soldier as suchlike comes—
  With a Fol rol dol rol di do.

'Twas sweet and fresh with buds of May,
Flowers springing from every spray;
And when he had supped the Old Soldier trolled
The song of youth that never grows old,
  Called Fol rol dol rol di do.

Most of him rags, and all of him lean,
And the belt round his belly drawn tightsome in,
He lifted his peaked old grizzled head,
And these were the very same words he said—
  A Fol-rol-dol-rol-*di*-do.

WALTER DE LA MARE

The Two Ravens

As I was walking all alone,
I heard two ravens making a moan,
The one unto the other say,
'Where shall we go and dine to-day?'

'In behind yon old turf-dyke,
I wot there lies a new-slain knight;
And nobody knows that he lies there,
But his hawk, his hound, and lady fair.

'His hound is to the hunting gone,
His hawk to fetch the wild fowl home,
His lady's taken another mate,
So we may make our dinner sweet.

'Ye'll sit on his white neck-bone
And I'll pick out his bonny blue eyes:
With one lock of his golden hair
We'll thatch our nest when it grows bare.

'Many a one for him makes moan,
But none shall know where he is gone.
O'er his white bones, when they are bare,
The wind shall blow for ever more.'

TRADITIONAL

I had Four Brothers

I HAD four brothers over the sea,
  Perrie, Merrie, Dixi, Domine;
And they each sent a present unto me.
  Petrum, Partrum, Paradisi, Tempore,
  Perrie, Merrie, Dixi, Domine.

The first sent a goose without a bone,
  Perrie, Merrie, Dixi, Domine;
The second sent a cherry without a stone,
  Petrum, Partrum, Paradisi, Tempore,
  Perrie, Merrie, Dixi, Domine.

The third sent a blanket without a thread,
  Perrie, Merrie, Dixi, Domine;
The fourth sent a book that no man could read,
  Petrum, Partrum, Paradisi, Tempore,
  Perrie, Merrie, Dixi, Domine.

When the cherry's in the blossom, there is no stone,
  Perrie, Merrie, Dixi, Domine;
When the goose is in the egg-shell, there is no bone,
  Petrum, Partrum, Paradisi, Tempore,
  Perrie, Merrie, Dixi, Domine.

When the wool's on the sheep's back, there is no thread,
  Perrie, Merrie, Dixi, Domine;
When the book's in the press, no man can read,
  Petrum, Partrum, Paradisi, Tempore,
  Perrie, Merrie, Dixi, Domine.

TRADITIONAL

Verses from 'A Countryman's Life'

OH, the sweet contentment
    The countryman doth find,
High trolollie lollie lo, high trolollie lee!
    That quiet contemplation
    Possesseth all my mind:
Then care away, and wend along with me.

    Our clothing is good sheepskins,
    Grey russet for our wives,
High trolollie lollie lo, high trolollie lee!
    'Tis warmth and not gay clothing
    That doth prolong our lives:
Then care away, and wend along with me.

    To recompense our tillage
    The heavens afford us showers,
High trolollie lollie lo, high trolollie lee!
    And for our sweet refreshments
    The earth affords us dowers:
Then care away, and wend along with me.

The ploughman, though he labour hard,
    Yet on the holy day,
High trolollie lollie lo, high trolollie lee!
    No Emperor so merrily
    Does pass his time away:
Then care away, and wend along with me.

    This is not half the happiness
    The countryman enjoys,
High trolollie lollie lo, high trolollie lee!
    Though others think they have as much,
    Yet he that says so lies:
Then care away, and wend along with me.

JOHN CHALKHILL

The Wandering Spectre

WOE'S me, woe's me,
The acorn's not yet fallen from the tree
That's to grow the wood,
That's to make the cradle,
That's to rock the bairn,
That's to grow a man,
That's to lay me.

TRADITIONAL

My Garden

THE lilac in my garden comes to bloom,
The apple, plum and cherry wait their hour,
The honeysuckle climbs from pole to pole—
And the rockery has a stone that's now a flower,
Jewelled by moss in every tiny hole!

Close to my lilac there's a small bird's nest
Of quiet, young, half-sleeping birds: but when
I look, each little rascal—five I've reckoned—
Opens a mouth so large and greedy then,
He swallows his own face in half a second!

W. H. DAVIES

A Dream

ONCE a dream did weave a shade
O'er my Angel-guarded bed,
That an emmet[1] lost its way
Where on grass methought I lay.

Troubled, wildered, and forlorn,
Dark, benighted, travel-worn,
Over many a tangled spray,
All heart-broke I heard her say:

'O, my children! do they cry?
Do they hear their father sigh?
Now they look abroad to see:
Now return and weep for me.'

Pitying, I dropped a tear;
But I saw a glow-worm near,
Who replied: 'What wailing wight
Calls the watchman of the night?

'I am set to light the ground,
While the beetle goes his round:
Follow now the beetle's hum;
Little wanderer, hie thee home.'

WILLIAM BLAKE

[1] Ant.

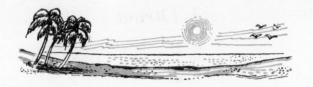

The Little Black Boy

MY mother bore me in the southern wild,
  And I am black, but O my soul is white;
White as an angel is the English child,
  But I am black, as if bereaved of light.

My mother taught me underneath a tree,
  And, sitting down before the heat of day,
She took me on her lap and kissèd me,
  And, pointing to the east, began to say:

'Look on the rising sun,—there God does live,
  And gives his light, and gives his heat away;
And flowers and trees and beasts and men receive
  Comfort in morning, joy in the noonday.

'And we are put on earth a little space,
  That we may learn to bear the beams of love;
And these black bodies and this sunburnt face
  Is but a cloud, and like a shady grove.

'For when our souls have learned the heat to bear,
  The cloud will vanish, we shall hear his voice,
Saying: "Come out from the grove, my love and care,
  And round my golden tent like lambs rejoice." '

Thus did my mother say, and kissèd me;
    And thus I say to little English boy.
When I from black, and he from white cloud free,
    And round the tent of God like lambs we joy,

I'll shade him from the heat, till he can bear
    To lean in joy upon our father's knee;
And then I'll stand and stroke his silver hair,
    And be like him, and he will then love me.

WILLIAM BLAKE

The Lord is my Shepherd

THE LORD is my shepherd;
    therefore can I lack nothing.
He shall feed me in a green pasture,
    and lead me forth beside the waters of comfort.
He shall convert my soul;
    and bring me forth in the paths of righteousness, for his
    Name's sake.
Yea, though I walk through the valley of the shadow of death,
I will fear no evil;
    for thou art with me; thy rod and thy staff comfort me.
Thou shalt prepare a table before me against them that trouble
me;
    thou hast anointed my head with oil, and my cup shall be
    full.
But thy loving-kindness and mercy shall follow me all the days
of my life;
    and I will dwell in the house of the Lord for ever.

PSALM 23

Travel

I SHOULD like to rise and go
Where the golden apples grow;—
Where below another sky
Parrot islands anchored lie,
And, watched by cockatoos and goats,
Lonely Crusoes building boats;—

Where in the sunshine reaching out
Eastern cities, miles about,
Are with mosque and minaret
Among sandy gardens set,
And the rich goods from near and far
Hang for sale in the bazaar;—

Where the Great Wall round China goes,
And on one side the desert blows,
And with bell and voice and drum,
Cities on the other hum;—
Where are forests, hot as fire,
Wide as England, tall as a spire,
Full of apes and coco-nuts
And the negro hunters' huts;—

Where the knotty crocodile
Lies and blinks in the Nile,
And the red flamingo flies
Hunting fish before his eyes;—
Where in jungles, near and far,
Man-devouring tigers are,

Lying close and giving ear
Lest the hunt be drawing near,
Or a comer-by be seen
Swinging in a palanquin;—

Where among the desert sands
Some deserted city stands,
All its children, sweep and prince,
Grown to manhood ages since,
Not a foot in street or house,
Not a stir of child or mouse,
And when kindly falls the night,
In all the town no spark of light.

There I'll come when I'm a man
With a camel caravan;
Light a fire in the gloom
Of some dusty dining-room;
See the pictures on the walls,
Heroes, fights, and festivals;
And in a corner find the toys
Of the old Egyptian boys.

ROBERT LOUIS STEVENSON

Bells

HARD as crystal,
  Clear as an icicle,
Is the tinkling sound
  Of a bell on a bicycle.

The bell in the clock
  That stands on the shelf
Slowly, sleepily
  Talks to itself.

The school bell is noisy
  And bangs like brass.
'Hurry up! Hurry up!
  Late for class!'

But deep and distant
  And peaceful to me
Are the bells I hear
  Below the sea.

Lying by the sea-shore
　On a calm day
Sometimes I hear them
　Far, far away.

With solemn tune
　In stately time
Under the water
　I hear them chime.

Why do the bells
　So stately sound?
For a sea-king dead,
　A sailor drowned?

Hark how they peal
　Far, far away!
Is it a mermaid's
　Marriage-day?

Do they ring for joy
　Or weeping or war,
Those bells I hear
　As I lie by the shore?

But merry or mournful
　So sweet to me
Are those dreamy bells
　Below the sea.

JAMES REEVES

Sheep

WHEN I was once in Baltimore,
  A man came up to me and cried,
'Come, I have eighteen hundred sheep
  And we sail on Tuesday's tide.'

'If you will sail with me, young man,
  I'll pay you fifty shillings down;
These eighteen hundred sheep I take
  From Baltimore to Glasgow town.'

He paid me fifty shillings down,
  I sailed with eighteen hundred sheep;
We soon had cleared the harbour's mouth,
  We soon were in the salt sea deep.

The first night we were out at sea
  Those sheep were quiet in their mind;
The second night they cried with fear—
  They smelt no pastures in the wind.

They sniffed, poor things, for their green fields,
  They cried so loud I could not sleep:
For fifty thousand shillings down
  I would not sail again with sheep.

W. H. DAVIES

W. H. DAVIES

portrait sketch by Augustus John (1918)

43

Goldenhair

LEAN out of the window,
  Goldenhair,
I heard you singing
  A merry air.

My book is closed;
  I read no more,
Watching the fire dance
  On the floor.

I have left my book;
  I have left my room,
For I heard you singing
  Through the gloom.

Singing and singing
  A merry air,
Lean out of the window,
  Goldenhair.

JAMES JOYCE

The Dove

I HAD a dove and the sweet dove died;
    And I have thought it died of grieving:
O, what could it grieve for?   Its feet were tied,
    With a silken thread of my own hand's weaving;
Sweet little red feet! why should you die—
Why should you leave me, sweet bird! why?
    You lived alone in the forest tree,
    Why, pretty thing! would you not live with me?
I kiss'd you oft, and gave you white peas;
    Why not live sweetly, as in the green trees?

JOHN KEATS

A Hymn for Saturday

Now's the time for mirth and play,
Saturday's an holiday:
Praise to Heaven unceasing yield,
I've found a lark's nest in the field.

A lark's nest, then your playmate begs
You'd spare herself and speckled eggs;
Soon she shall ascend and sing
Your praises to the eternal King.

CHRISTOPHER SMART

Under the Greenwood Tree

UNDER the greenwood tree,
Who loves to lie with me,
And turn his merry note
Unto the sweet bird's throat,
Come hither, come hither, come hither:
    Here shall he see
    No enemy
But winter and rough weather.

Who doth ambition shun,
And loves to live i' the sun,
Seeking the food he eats,
And pleased with what he gets,
Come hither, come hither, come hither:
    Here shall he see
    No enemy
But winter and rough weather.

WILLIAM SHAKESPEARE

Now the Hungry Lion Roars

Now the hungry lion roars,
And the wolf behowls the moon;
Whilst the heavy ploughman snores,
All with weary task fordone.
Now the wasted brands do glow,
Whilst the screech-owl, screeching loud,
Puts the wretch that lies in woe
In remembrance of a shroud.
Now it is the time of night
That the graves, all gaping wide,
Every one lets forth his sprite,
In the church-way paths to glide:
And we fairies, that do run
By the triple Hecate's[1] team,
From the presence of the sun,
Following darkness like a dream,
Now are frolic; not a mouse
Shall disturb this hallow'd house:
I am sent with broom before,
To sweep the dust behind the door.

WILLIAM SHAKESPEARE

[1] Queen of Witches in Heaven, Earth and Hell.

Hunting Song

THE dusky night rides down the sky
    And ushers in the morn;
The hounds all join in glorious cry,
    The Huntsman winds his horn:
      And a hunting we will go.

The wife around her husband throws
    Her arms, and begs him stay;
'My dear, it rains, and hails, and snows,
    You will not hunt to-day.'
      But a hunting we will go.

'A brushing fox in yonder wood,
    Secure to find we seek;
For why, I carried sound and good
    A cartload there last week.'
      And a hunting we will go.

Away he goes, he flies the rout,
    Their steeds all spur and switch;
Some are thrown in, and some thrown out,
    And some thrown in the ditch:
      But a hunting we will go.

At length his strength to faintness worn,
    Poor Reynard ceases flight;
Then hungry, homeward we return,
    To feast away the night:
      Then a drinking we will go.

HENRY FIELDING

A HUNTING SCENE
from an early 18th-century engraving

Buy Broom Buzzums

If you want a buzzum
For to sweep your hoose,
Come to me, maw hinnies,[1]
Ye may ha' your choose.
  Buy broom buzzums,
    Buy them when they're new,
  Fine heather-bred 'uns,
    Better never grew.

If Aw had a horse
Aw wad hev a cairt;
If Aw had a wife
She wad tyek me pairt.[2]
  Buy broom buzzums . . .

Had Aw but a wife,
Aw care not what she be,
If she's but a woman
That's enough for me.
  Buy broom buzzums . . .

If she liked a droppie
Her and I'd agree,
If she didn't like it
There's the mair for me.
  Buy broom buzzums . . .

NORTHUMBRIAN FOLK SONG

[1] My honeys.   [2] Take my part.

Blow, blow, thou Winter Wind

BLOW, blow, thou winter wind,
Thou art not so unkind
  As man's ingratitude;
Thy tooth is not so keen,
Because thou art not seen,
  Although thy breath be rude.

Heigh-ho! sing, heigh-ho! unto the green holly:
Most friendship is feigning, most loving mere folly.
  Then heigh-ho! the holly!
  This life is most jolly.

Freeze, freeze, thou bitter sky,
That dost not bite so nigh
  As benefits forgot:
Though thou the waters warp,[1]
Thy sting is not so sharp
  As friend remember'd not.

Heigh-ho! sing, heigh-ho! unto the green holly:
Most friendship is feigning, most loving mere folly.
  Then heigh-ho! the holly!
  This life is most jolly.

WILLIAM SHAKESPEARE

[1] Harden.

Over Hill, Over Dale

OVER hill, over dale,
Thorough bush, thorough brier,
Over park, over pale,
Thorough flood, thorough fire,
I do wander everywhere,
Swifter than the moonës sphere;
And I serve the fairy queen,
To dew her orbs upon the green:

The cowslips tall her pensioners be;
In their gold coats spots you see;
Those be rubies, fairy favours,
In those freckles live their savours:
I must go seek some dew-drops here,
And hang a pearl in every cowslip's ear.

WILLIAM SHAKESPEARE

Where the Bee Sucks

WHERE the bee sucks, there suck I,
In a cowslip's bell I lie,
There I couch when owls do cry;
On the bat's back I do fly
After summer merrily.
Merrily, merrily, shall I live now
Under the blossom that hangs on the bough.

WILLIAM SHAKESPEARE

Come unto these Yellow Sands

COME unto these yellow sands,
   and then take hands:
Curtsied when you have and kissed
   the wild waves whist:
Foot it featly here and there,
And sweet sprites the burden bear.
Hark, hark, bow wow:
   the watch-dogs bark, bow wow.
Hark, hark, I hear
   the strain of strutting Chanticleer
Cry cock-a-diddle dow!

WILLIAM SHAKESPEARE

Full Fathom Five

FULL fathom five thy father lies;
Of his bones are coral made:
Those are pearls that were his eyes:
Nothing of him that doth fade,
But doth suffer a sea-change
Into something rich and strange.
Sea-nymphs hourly ring his knell:
   Ding-Dong.
Hark! now I hear them,—ding-dong, bell.

WILLIAM SHAKESPEARE

York, York for my Money

As I went through the North country,
The fashions of the world to see,
I sought for merry company
  To go to the City of London.
And when to the City of York I came,
I found good company in the same,
As well disposed to every game
  As if it had been at London.

York, York, for my money;
Of all the cities that ever I see
For merry pastime and company,
  Except the City of London.

YORK
from an Elizabethan engraving

And in that City what I saw then?
Knights and Squires and gentlemen
A shooting went for matches ten,
    As if it had been at London.
And they shot for twenty pounds a bow,
Besides great cheer they did bestow,
I never saw a gallanter show,
    Except I had been at London.

York, York for my money;
Of all the cities that ever I see
For merry pastime and company
    Except the City of London.

WILLIAM ELDERTON

(Verses from a ballad sung to the tune of *Greensleeves*.)

Hark, Hark! the Lark

HARK, hark! the lark at Heaven's gate sings,
    And Phoebus 'gins arise,
His steeds to water at those springs
    On chaliced flowers that lies;
And winking mary-buds begin
    To ope their golden eyes;
With every thing that pretty is,
    My lady sweet, arise:
        Arise, arise!

WILLIAM SHAKESPEARE

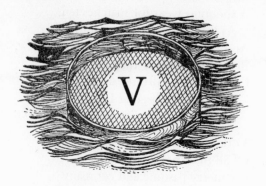

The Jumblies

I

THEY went to sea in a Sieve, they did,
  In a Sieve they went to sea:
In spite of all their friends could say,
On a winter's morn, on a stormy day,
  In a Sieve they went to sea!
And when the Sieve turned round and round,
And every one cried, 'You'll all be drowned!'
They called aloud, 'Our Sieve ain't big,
But we don't care a button! we don't care a fig!
  In a Sieve we'll go to sea!'
    Far and few, far and few,
      Are the lands where the Jumblies live;
      Their heads are green, and their hands are blue,
        And they went to sea in a Sieve.

They sailed away in a Sieve, they did,
  In a Sieve they sailed so fast,
With only a beautiful pea-green veil
Tied with a riband by way of a sail,
  To a small tobacco-pipe mast;
And every one said, who saw them go,
'O won't they be soon upset, you know!
For the sky is dark, and the voyage is long,
And happen what may, it's extremely wrong
  In a Sieve to sail so fast!'
    Far and few, far and few,
      Are the lands where the Jumblies live;
    Their heads are green, and their hands are blue,
    And they went to sea in a Sieve.

The water it soon came in, it did,
  The water it soon came in;
So to keep them dry, they wrapped their feet
In a pinky paper all folded neat,
  And they fastened it down with a pin.
And they passed the night in a crockery-jar,
And each of them said, 'How wise we are!
Though the sky be dark, and the voyage be long,
Yet we never can think we were rash or wrong,
  While round in our Sieve we spin!'
    Far and few, far and few,
      Are the lands where the Jumblies live;
    Their heads are green, and their hands are blue,
    And they went to sea in a Sieve.

And all night long they sailed away;
  And when the sun went down,
They whistled and warbled a moony song
To the echoing sound of a coppery gong,
  In the shade of the mountains brown.
'O Timballo! How happy we are,
When we live in a sieve and a crockery-jar,
And all night long in the moonlight pale,
We sail away with a pea-green sail,
  In the shade of the mountains brown!'
    Far and few, far and few,
      Are the lands where the Jumblies live;
     Their heads are green, and their hands are blue,
      And they went to sea in a Sieve.

They sailed to the Western Sea, they did,
  To a land all covered with trees,
And they bought an Owl, and a useful Cart,
And a pound of Rice, and a Cranberry Tart,
  And a hive of silvery Bees.
And they bought a Pig, and some green Jack-daws,
And a lovely Monkey with lollipop paws,
And forty bottles of Ring-Bo-Ree,
  And no end of Stilton Cheese.
    Far and few, far and few,
      Are the lands where the Jumblies live;
     Their heads are green and their hands are blue,
      And they went to sea in a Sieve.

And in twenty years they all came back,
    In twenty years or more,
And every one said, 'How tall they've grown!
For they've been to the Lakes, and the Terrible Zone,
    And the hills of the Chankly Bore';
And they drank their health, and gave them a feast
Of dumplings made of beautiful yeast;
And every one said, 'If we only live,
We too will go to sea in a Sieve,—
    To the hills of the Chankly Bore!'
        Far and few, far and few,
            Are the lands where the Jumblies live;
        Their heads are green, and their hands are blue,
            And they went to sea in a Sieve.

EDWARD LEAR

THE ADORATION OF THE MAGI
from a medieval woodcut

A Child this Day is Born

A CHILD this day is born,
A child of high renown,
Most worthy of a sceptre,
A sceptre and a crown:

Nowell, Nowell, Nowell,
Nowell, sing all we may,
Because the King of all kings
Was born this blessèd day.

60

These tidings shepherds heard,
In field watching their fold,
Were by an angel unto them
That night revealed and told:

To whom the angel spoke,
Saying, 'Be not afraid;
Be glad, poor silly[1] shepherds—
Why are you so dismayed?

For lo! I bring you tidings
Of gladness and of mirth,
Which cometh to all people by
This holy infant's birth':

Then there was with the angel
A host incontinent[2]
Of heavenly bright soldiers,
Which from the Highest was sent:

Lauding the Lord our God,
And his celestial King;
All glory be in Paradise,
This heavenly host did sing:

And as the angel told them,
So to them did appear;
They found the young child, Jesus Christ,
With Mary, his mother dear.

TRADITIONAL

[1] Simple.   [2] Innumerable.

Green Broom

THERE was an old man lived out in the wood,
   His trade was a-cutting of Broom, green Broom;
He had but one son without thrift, without good,
   Who lay in his bed till 'twas noon, bright noon.

The old man awoke, one morning and spoke;
   He swore he would fire the room, that room,
If his John would not rise and open his eyes,
   And away to the wood to cut Broom, green Broom.

So Johnny arose, and he slipped on his clothes,
   And away to the wood to cut Broom, green Broom;
He sharpened his knives, for once he contrives
   To cut a great bundle of Broom, green Broom;

When Johnny passed under a lady's fine house,
   Passed under a lady's fine room, fine room,
She called to her maid, 'Go fetch me,' she said,
   'Go fetch me the boy that sells Broom, green Broom.'

When Johnny came into the lady's fine house,
   And stood in the lady's fine room, fine room,
'Young Johnny,' she said, 'will you give up your trade,
   And marry a lady in bloom, full bloom?'

Johnny gave his consent, and to church they both went,
   And he wedded the lady in bloom, full bloom;
At market and fair, all folks do declare,
   There is none like the Boy that sold Broom, green Broom.

TRADITIONAL

Praise Ye the Lord

PRAISE ye the Lord.
Praise ye the Lord from the heavens;
Praise him in the heights.
Praise ye him, all his angels;
Praise ye him, all his hosts.
Praise ye him, sun and moon;
Praise him, all ye stars of light.
Praise him, ye heavens of heavens,
And ye waters that be above the heavens.
   Let them praise the name of the Lord:
   For he commanded, and they were created.
   He hath also stablished them for ever and ever;
   He hath made a decree which shall not pass.
Praise the Lord from the earth,
Ye dragons, and all deeps;
Fire and hail, snow and vapours,
Stormy wind fulfilling his word;
Mountains and all hills,
Fruitful trees and all cedars,
Beasts and all cattle,
Creeping things and flying fowl;
Kings of the earth and all people,

Princes and all judges of the earth;
Both young men and maidens,
Old men and children,
　　Let them praise the name of the Lord:
　　For his name alone is excellent;
　　His glory is above the earth and heaven.
　　He also exalteth the horn of his people,
　　The praise of all his saints;
　　Even of the children of Israel, a people near unto him.
　　　Praise ye the Lord.

PSALM 148

Hynd Horn

IN Scotland there was a baby born,
　　With a hey lilly loo and a how lo lan,
And his name it was called young Hynd Horn,
　　And the birk and the broom blooms bonny.

He sent a letter to our King,
　　With a hey lilly loo . . .
That he was in love with his daughter Jean,
　　And the birk . . .

64

The King an angry man was he;
He sent young Hynd Horn to the sea.

He's given to her a silver wand,
With seven living laverocks[1] sitting thereon.

She's given to him a diamond ring,
With seven bright diamonds set therein.

'When this ring grows pale and wan,
You may know by it my love is gone.'

One day as he looked his ring upon,
He saw the diamonds pale and wan.

He left the sea and came to land,
And the first that he met was an old beggar-man.

'What news, what news?' said young Hynd Horn,
'No news, no news,' said the old beggar-man.

'No news,' said the beggar, 'no news at all,
But there is a wedding in the King's Hall.'

'Wilt thou lend me thy begging coat?
And I'll lend thee my scarlet cloak.

'Wilt thou lend me thy beggar's ring?
And I'll give thee my steed to ride upon.'

The old beggar-man was bound for to ride,
But young Hynd Horn was bound for the bride.

[1] Seven larks carved or drawn in a life-like way.

When he came to the King's gate,
He sought a drink for Hynd Horn's sake.

The bride came down with a glass of wine,
When he drank out the glass, and dropped in the ring.

'O, got ye this by sea or by land?
Or got thou it off a dead man's hand?'

'I got it not by sea, but I got it by land,
For I got it out of your fair hand.'

'O, I'll cast off my satin gown,
And follow you from town to town.

'I'll take the fine gold from my hair,
And follow you for ever mair.'

The bridegroom wedded the bride that day,
  With a hey lilly loo and a how lo lan,
But young Hynd Horn did steal her away,
  And the birk and the broom blooms bonny.

TRADITIONAL

Make We Merry

MAKE we merry, both more and less,
For now is the time of Christëmas.

Let no man come into this hall,
Nor groom, nor page, nor yet marshall,
But that some sport he bring withal.

If that he say he cannot sing,
Some other sport then let him bring,
That it may please at this feasting.

If he say he naught can do,
Then, for my love, ask him no mo'
But to the stocks then let him go.

Make we merry, both more and less,
For now is the time of Christëmas.

TRADITIONAL

Dirge for Robin Hood

WEEP, weep, ye woodmen, wail;
Your hands with sorrow wring!
Your master Robin Hood lies dead,
Therefore sigh as you sing.

Here lies his primer and his beads,
His bent bow and his arrows keen,
His good sword and his holy cross.
Now cast on flowers fresh and green;

And, as they fall, shed tears and say
Well-a, well-a-day! well-a, well-a-day!
Thus cast ye flowers, and sing,
And on to Wakefield take your way.

ANTHONY MUNDAY

Henry Martyn

In merry Scotland, in merry Scotland
   There lived brothers three;
They all did cast lots which of them should go
   A-robbing upon the salt sea.

The lot it fell on Henry Martyn,
   The youngest of the three;
That he should go rob on the salt, salt sea,
   To maintain his brothers and he.

He had not sailed a long winter's night,
   Nor yet a short winter's day,
Before that he met with a lofty old ship,
   Come sailing along that way.

'Stand off! stand off!' said Henry Martyn,
   'For you shall not pass by me;
For I am a robber all on the salt seas,
   To maintain us brothers three.'

'Stand off! stand off!' the captain he cried,
   'The life-guards they are aboard.
My cannons are loaden with powder and shot;
   And every man hath a sword.'

For three long hours they merrily fought,
   For hours they fought full three;
At last a deep wound got Henry Martyn,
   And down by the mast fell he.

'Twas broadside against a broadside then,
  And at it the which should win,
A shot in the gallant ship bored a hole,
  And then did the water rush in.

Bad news, bad news for old England,
  Bad news has come to the town,
For a rich merchant's vessel is cast away
  And all her brave seamen drown.

Bad news, bad news through the London street,
  Bad news has come to the King!
The lives of his guard they be all a-lost,
  O the tidings be sad that I bring.

TRADITIONAL

Song of the Western Men

A GOOD sword and a trusty hand!
  A merry heart and true!
King James's men shall understand
  What Cornish lads can do.

And have they fixed the where and when?
  And shall Trelawney die?
Here's twenty thousand Cornish men
  Will know the reason why!

Out spake their captain brave and bold,
  A merry wight was he:
'If London Tower were Michael's hold,
  We'll set Trelawney free!

'We'll cross the Tamar, land to land,
   The Severn is no stay—
With "one and all" and hand in hand,
   And who shall bid us nay?

'And when we come to London Wall,
   A pleasant sight to view,
Come forth! come forth, ye cowards all,
   Here's men as good as you.

'Trelawney he's in keep and hold,
   Trelawney he may die—
But here's twenty thousand Cornish bold
   Will know the reason why!'

                    ROBERT STEVEN HAWKER

THE TOWER OF LONDON
from a 17th-century engraving

The Death of Admiral Benbow

COME all you seamen bold and draw near, and draw near,
Come all you seamen bold and draw near.
It's of an admiral's fame, O brave Benbow was his name,
How he fought all on the main you shall hear, you shall hear.

Brave Benbow he set sail for to fight, for to fight,
Brave Benbow he set sail for to fight;
Brave Benbow he set sail with a fine and pleasant gale,
But his captains they turned tail in a fright, in a fright.

Says Kirby unto Wade, we will run, we will run,
Says Kirby unto Wade, we will run:
For I value no disgrace, nor the losing of my place,
But the enemy I won't face nor his guns, nor his guns.

The Ruby and Benbow fought the French, fought the French,
The Ruby and Benbow fought the French;
They fought them up and down, till the blood came trickling
down,
Till the blood came trickling down where they lay, where they
lay.

Brave Benbow lost his legs by chain-shot, by chain-shot,
Brave Benbow lost his legs by chain-shot:
Brave Benbow lost his legs, and all on his stumps he begs—
Fight on my English lads, 'tis our lot, 'tis our lot.

The surgeon dressed his wounds; cries Benbow, cries Benbow:
The surgeon dressed his wounds; cries Benbow—
Let a cradle now in haste on the quarter deck be placed,
That the enemy I may face till I die, till I die.

TRADITIONAL

ADMIRAL BENBOW

from a painting by Sir Godfrey Kneller (about 1700)

Bonnie George Campbell

HIE upon Hielands
And low upon Tay,
Bonnie George Campbell
Rade out on a day.
Saddled and bridled
And gallant rade he;
Hame came his gude horse,
But never cam he!

Out cam his auld mither
Greeting fu' sair,
And out cam his bonnie bride
Rivin' her hair.
Saddled and bridled
And booted rade he;
Toom[1] hame cam the saddle,
But never cam he!

'My meadow lies green,
And my corn is unshorn;
My barn is to big,[2]
And my babie's unborn.'
Saddled and bridled
And booted rade he;
Toom hame cam the saddle,
But never cam he!

TRADITIONAL

[1] Empty.   [2] Be built.

The Owl and the Pussy-Cat

THE Owl and the Pussy-Cat went to sea
In a beautiful pea-green boat,
They took some honey, and plenty of money,
Wrapped up in a five-pound note.
The Owl looked up to the stars above,
And sang to a small guitar,
'O lovely Pussy! O Pussy, my love,
What a beautiful Pussy you are,
            You are,
            You are!
What a beautiful Pussy you are!'

Pussy said to the Owl, 'You elegant fowl!
How charmingly sweet you sing!
O let us be married! too long we have tarried:
But what shall we do for a ring?'

They sailed away for a year and a day,
To the land where the Bong-tree grows,
And there in a wood a Piggy-wig stood,
With a ring at the end of his nose.
        His nose,
        His nose,
With a ring at the end of his nose.

'Dear Pig, are you willing to sell for one shilling
Your ring?' Said the Piggy, 'I will.'
So they took it away, and were married next day
By the Turkey who lives on the hill.
They dined on mince, and slices of quince,
Which they ate with a runcible spoon;
And hand in hand, on the edge of the sand,
They danced in the light of the moon,
        The moon,
        The moon,
They danced by the light of the moon.

EDWARD LEAR

Tit for Tat

HAVE you been catching of fish, Tom Noddy?
    Have you snared a weeping hare?
Have you whistled, 'No Nunny,' and gunned a poor bunny,
    Or a blinded bird of the air?

Have you trod like a murderer through the green woods,
    Through the dewy deep dingles and glooms,
While every small creature screamed shrill to Dame Nature,
    'He comes—and he comes!'?

Wonder I very much do, Tom Noddy,
    If ever, when you are a-roam,
An Ogre from space will stoop a lean face,
    And lug you home:

Lug you home over his fence, Tom Noddy,
    Of thorn-sticks nine yards high,
With your bent knees strung round his old iron gun
    And your head dan-dangling by:

And hang you up stiff on a hook, Tom Noddy,
    From a stone-cold pantry shelf,
Whence your eyes will glare in an empty stare,
    Till you're cooked yourself!

WALTER DE LA MARE

The Three Unlucky Men

NEAR Wookey Hole in days gone by
   Lived three unlucky men.
The first fell down a Treacle Mine
   And never stirred again.

The second had no better fate
   And he too is no more.
He fell into a Custard Lake
   And could not get to shore.

The third poor fellow, sad to say,
   He had no fairer luck,
For he climbed up a Porridge Hill
   And half-way down got stuck.

Alas, alas! man is but grass,
   Let life be short or long;
And all the birds cried 'Fancy that!'
   To hear this merry song.

JAMES REEVES

The Quangle Wangle's Hat

ON top of the Crumpetty Tree
   The Quangle Wangle sat,
But his face you could not see,
   On account of his Beaver Hat.
For his Hat was a hundred and two feet wide,
With ribbons and bibbons on every side,
And bells, and buttons, and loops, and lace,
So that nobody ever could see the face
     Of the Quangle Wangle Quee.

The Quangle Wangle said
   To himself on the Crumpetty Tree,
'Jam; and jelly; and bread;
   Are the best of food for me!
But the longer I live on this Crumpetty Tree,
The plainer than ever it seems to me
That very few people come this way,
And that life on the whole is far from gay!'
     Said the Quangle Wangle Quee.

But there came to the Crumpetty Tree
   Mr and Mrs Canary;
And they said, 'Did ever you see
   Any spot so charmingly airy?
May we build a nest on your lovely Hat?
Mr Quangle Wangle, grant us that!
O please let us come and build a nest
Of whatever material suits you best,
     Mr Quangle Wangle Quee!'

And besides, to the Crumpetty Tree
   Came the Stork, the Duck, and the Owl;
The Snail and the Bumble-Bee,
   The Frog, and the Fimble Fowl
(The Fimble Fowl with a corkscrew leg);
And all of them said, 'We humbly beg,
We may build our homes on your lovely Hat,
Mr Quangle Wangle, grant us that!
    Mr Quangle Wangle Quee!'

And the Golden Grouse came there,
   And the Pobble who hast no toes,
And the small Olympian bear
   And the Dong with a luminous nose.
And the Blue Baboon, who played the flute,
And the Orient Calf from the Land of Tute,
And the Attery Squash and the Bisky Bat,
All came and built on the lovely Hat
    Of the Quangle Wangle Quee.

And the Quangle Wangle said
   To himself on the Crumpetty Tree,
'When all these creatures move
   What a wonderful noise there'll be!'
And at night by the light of the Mulberry Moon
They danced to the Flute of the Blue Baboon
On the broad green leaves of the Crumpetty Tree,
And all were as happy as happy could be,
    With the Quangle Wangle Quee.

EDWARD LEAR

Miss T.

Iᴛ's a very odd thing—
  As odd as can be—
That whatever Miss T. eats
  Turns into Miss T.;
Porridge and apples,
  Mince, muffins and mutton,
Jam, junket, jumbles—
  Not a rap, not a button
It matters; the moment
  They're out of her plate,
Though shared by Miss Butcher
  And sour Mr Bate;
Tiny and cheerful
  And neat as can be,
Whatever Miss T. eats
  Turns into Miss T.

WALTER DE LA MARE

Poor Henry

THICK in its glass
   The physic stands,
Poor Henry lifts
   Distracted hands;
His round cheek wans
   In the candlelight,
To smell that smell!
   To see that sight!

Finger and thumb
   Clinch his small nose,
A gurgle, a gasp,
   And down it goes;
Scowls Henry now;
   But mark that cheek,
Sleek with the bloom
   Of health next week!

WALTER DE LA MARE

The Derby Ram

As I went down to Derby town,
  'Twas on a market day,
And there I met the finest ram
  Was ever fed on hay.
    Riddle to my rye,
    Riddle to my rye.

The wool upon this ram's back,
  It grew up to the sky;
The eagles built their nests in it.
  I heard the young ones cry.
    Riddle to my rye,
    Riddle to my rye.

The horns upon this ram's head,
  They grew up to the moon.
A man climbed up in April
  And never came down till June.
    Riddle to my rye,
    Riddle to my rye.

The wool upon this ram's tail
  Was very fine and thin,
Took all the girls in Derby town
  Full seven years to spin.
    Riddle to my rye,
    Riddle to my rye.

This ram he had four mighty feet
  And on them he did stand,
And every foot that he had got
  Did cover an acre of land.
    Riddle to my rye,
    Riddle to my rye.

And every tooth this ram had
  Was hollow as a horn.
They took one out and measured it,
  It held a barrel of corn.
    Riddle to my rye,
    Riddle to my rye.

And if you don't believe me
  And think it is a lie,
Then you go down to Derby town
  And see as well as I.
    Riddle to my rye,
    Riddle to my rye.

TRADITIONAL

The Witch Stepmother

'I WAS but seven years old
    When my mother she did die;
My father married the very worst woman
    The world did ever see.

For she has made me the loathly worm[1]
    That lies at the foot of the tree,
And my sister Maisry she's made
    The mackerel of the sea.

And every Saturday at noon
    The mackerel comes to me,
And she takes my loathly head
    And lays it on her knee,
She combs it with a silver comb,
    And washes it in the sea.

Seven knights have I slain,
    Since I lay at the foot of the tree,
And were ye not my own father,
    The eighth one ye should be.'

The father sent for his lady,
    As fast as send could he:
'Where is my son that ye sent from me,
    And my daughter Lady Maisry?'

[1] Serpent.

85

'Your son is at our king's court,
    Serving for meat and fee;
And your daughter's at our queen's court,
    A waiting-woman is she.'

'Ye lie, ye ill woman,
    So loud I hear ye lie:
My son's the loathly worm,
    That lies at the foot of the tree,
And my daughter Lady Maisry
    Is the mackerel of the sea!'

She has taken a silver wand,
    And given him strokes three,
And he's started up the bravest knight
    That ever your eyes did see.

She has taken a small horn,
    And loud and shrill blew she,
And all the fish came unto her
    But the proud mackerel of the sea:
'Ye shaped me once an unseemly shape
    Ye shall never more shape me.'

He has sent to the wood
    For whins and for hawthorn,
And he has taken that gay lady
    And there he did her burn.

TRADITIONAL

86

A WITCH AND HER FAMILIARS
from a 16th-century manuscript

87

If All the World were Paper

IF all the world were paper,
  And all the sea were ink,
And all the trees were bread and cheese,
  What should we do for drink?

If all the world were sand-o,
  Oh, then what should we lack-o?
If, as they say, there were no clay,
  How should we take tobacco?

If all our vessels ran-a,
  If none but had a crack,
If Spanish apes ate all the grapes,
  How should we do for sack?[1]

If friars had no bald pates,
  Nor nuns had no dark cloisters;
If all the seas were beans and peas,
  How should we do for oysters?

If all things were eternal,
  And nothing their end bringing;
If this should be, then how should we
  Here make an end of singing?

TRADITIONAL

[1] Sherry.

The Ride-By-Nights

Up on their brooms the Witches stream,
Crooked and black in the crescent's gleam;
One foot high, and one foot low,
Bearded, cloaked, and cowled, they go,
'Neath Charlie's Wain they twitter and tweet,
And away they swarm 'neath the Dragon's feet.
With a whoop and a flutter they swing and sway,
And surge pell-mell down the Milky Way.
Betwixt the legs of the glittering Chair
They hover and squeak in the empty air.
Then round they swoop past the glimmering Lion
To where Sirius barks behind huge Orion;
Up, then, and over to wheel amain,
Under the silver, and home again.

WALTER DE LA MARE

Turtle Soup

BEAUTIFUL soup, so rich and green,
Waiting in a hot tureen!
Who for such dainties would not stoop?
Soup of the evening, beautiful soup!
Soup of the evening, beautiful soup!
    Beau—ootiful soo—oop!
    Beau—ootiful soo—oop!
Soo—oop of the e—e—evening,
    Beautiful, beautiful soup!

Beautiful soup! Who cares for fish,
Game, or any other dish?
Who would not give all else for two p
ennyworth only of beautiful soup?
Pennyworth only of beautiful soup?
    Beau—ootiful soo—oop!
    Beau—ootiful soo—oop!
Soo—oop of the e—e—evening,
    Beautiful, beauti—FUL SOUP!

LEWIS CARROLL

90

The Umbrella Trees

UNDER the umbrageous[1] umbrella trees
Easily the elephant eats at his ease;
The horn of the hunter is heard on the hill,
And the hounds are a-harking in harmony shrill.

ANONYMOUS

[1] Shady.

Jabberwocky

'TWAS brillig, and the slithy toves
   Did gyre and gimble in the wabe;
All mimsy were the borogoves,
   And the mome raths outgrabe.

'Beware the Jabberwock, my son!
   The jaws that bite, the claws that catch!
Beware the Jubjub bird, and shun
   The frumious Bandersnatch!'

He took his vorpal sword in hand:
   Long time the manxome foe he sought—
So rested he by the Tumtum tree,
   And stood awhile in thought.

And as in uffish thought he stood,
   The Jabberwock, with eyes of flame,
Came whiffling through the tulgey wood
   And burbled as it came!

One, two! One, two! And through and through
    The vorpal blade went snicker-snack!
He left it dead, and with its head
    He went galumphing back.

'And hast thou slain the Jabberwock?
    Come to my arms, my beamish boy!
A frabjous day! Callooh callay!'
    He chortled in his joy.

'Twas brillig, and the slithy toves
    Did gyre and gimble in the wabe;
All mimsy were the borogoves,
    And the mome raths outgrabe.

LEWIS CARROLL

The Big Baboon

THE Big Baboon is found upon
    The plains of Cariboo:
He goes about with nothing on
    (A shocking thing to do).

But if he dressed respectably
    And let his whiskers grow,
How like this Big Baboon would be
    To Mr So-and-so!

HILAIRE BELLOC

I Saw a Peacock

I SAW a peacock with a fiery tail
I saw a blazing comet drop down hail
I saw a cloud wrapped with ivy round
I saw an oak creep on along the ground
I saw a serpent swallow up a whale
I saw the sea brim full of ale
I saw a Venice glass five fathom deep
I saw a well full of men's tears that weep
I saw red eyes all of a flaming fire
I saw a house bigger than the moon and higher
I saw the sun at twelve o'clock at night
I saw the man that saw this wondrous sight.

TRADITIONAL

93

Jim

THERE was a Boy whose name was Jim;
His Friends were very good to him.
They gave him Tea, and Cakes, and Jam,
And slices of delicious Ham,
And Chocolate with pink inside,
And little Tricycles to ride,
And read him Stories through and through,

And even took him to the Zoo—
But there it was the dreadful Fate
Befell him, which I now relate.
You know—at least you *ought* to know,
For I have often told you so—
That Children never are allowed
To leave their Nurses in a Crowd;

Now this was Jim's especial Foible,
He ran away when he was able.
And on this inauspicious day
He slipped his hand and ran away!
He hadn't gone a yard when—Bang!

With open Jaws a Lion sprang,
And hungrily began to eat
The Boy: beginning at his feet.
Now just imagine how it feels
When first your toes and then your heels,
And then by gradual degrees
Your shins and ankles, calves and knees,
Are slowly eaten, bit by bit.
No wonder Jim detested it!
No wonder that he shouted, 'Hi!'
The Honest Keeper heard his cry,

Though very fat he almost ran
To help the little gentleman.

'Ponto!' he ordered as he came
(For Ponto was the Lion's name)
'Ponto!' he cried, with angry Frown,
'Let go, Sir! Down, Sir! Put it down!'

The Lion made a sudden Stop,
He let the dainty Morsel drop,
And slunk reluctant to his Cage,
Snarling with Disappointed Rage.
But when he bent him over Jim,
The Honest Keeper's eyes were dim.
The Lion having reached his Head,
The Miserable Boy was dead!
When Nurse informed his Parents, they

Original illustrations by B.T.B

96

Were more Concerned than I can say:—
His Mother, as she dried her eyes,
Said, 'Well—it gives me no surprise,
He would not do as he was told!'
His Father, who was self-controlled,
Bade all the children round attend
To James' miserable end,
And always keep a-hold of Nurse
For fear of finding something worse.

HILAIRE BELLOC

The Old Lady of Chertsey

THERE was an old lady of Chertsey,
Who made a remarkable curtsey;
  She twirled round and round,
  Till she sunk underground,
Which distressed all the people of Chertsey.

EDWARD LEAR

The Hippopotamus

I SHOOT the Hippopotamus
 With bullets made of platinum,
Because if I use leaden ones,
 His hide is sure to flatten 'em.

HILAIRE BELLOC

Stand! Who Goes There?

WATCH	Stand! who goes there?
	We charge you appear
	'Fore our constable here,
	In the name of the Man in the Moon.
	To us billmen relate,
	Why you stagger so late,
	And how you come drunk so soon.
PAGES	What are ye, scabs?
WATCH	The watch:
	This the constable.
PAGES	A patch!
CONSTABLE	Knock 'em down unless they all stand;
	If any run away,
	'Tis the old watchman's play,
	To reach him a bill of his hand.
PAGES	O gentlemen, hold,
	Your gowns freeze with cold,
	And your rotten teeth dance in your head.
	Wine nothing shall cost ye;
	Nor huge fires to roast ye;
	Then soberly let us be led.
CONSTABLE	Come, my brown bills, we'll roar,
	Bounce loud at tavern door.
ALL	And i' th' morning steal all to bed.

JOHN LYLY

Drawing by Lewis Carroll

Father William

'You are old, Father William,' the young man said,
  'And your hair has become very white;
And yet you incessantly stand on your head—
  Do you think, at your age, it is right?'

'In my youth,' Father William replied to his son,
  'I feared it might injure the brain;
But now that I'm perfectly sure I have none,
  Why, I do it again and again.'

'You are old,' said the youth, 'as I mentioned before,
  And have grown most uncommonly fat;
Yet you turned a back-somersault in at the door—
  Pray, what is the reason of that?'

'In my youth,' said the sage, as he shook his grey locks,
  'I kept all my limbs very supple
By the use of this ointment—one shilling the box—
  Allow me to sell you a couple?'

Drawing by Lewis Carroll

'You are old,' said the youth, 'and your jaws are too weak
    For anything tougher than suet;
Yet you finished the goose, with the bones and the beak—
    Pray, how did you manage to do it?'

'In my youth,' said his father, 'I took to the law,
    And argued each case with my wife;
And the muscular strength, which it gave to my jaw,
    Has lasted the rest of my life.'

'You are old,' said the youth, 'one would hardly suppose
    That your eye was as steady as ever;
Yet you balanced an eel on the end of your nose—
    What made you so awfully clever?'

'I have answered three questions, and that is enough,'
    Said his father; 'don't give yourself airs!
Do you think I can listen all day to such stuff?
    Be off, or I'll kick you down stairs!'

LEWIS CARROLL

The Old Man in a Barge

THERE was an old man in a barge,
Whose nose was exceedingly large;
 But in fishing by night,
 It supported a light,
Which helped that old man in a barge.

EDWARD · LEAR

A Milkmaid

TWO legs sat upon three legs,
With four legs standing by;
Four were then drawn by ten:
Read my riddle ye can't,
However much ye try.

TRADITIONAL

Gibberish

INFIRTARIS,
Inoaknoneis.
Inmudeelsare,
Inclaynoneis.
Goateativy,
Mareeatoats.

TRADITIONAL

The Pied Piper of Hamelin

HAMELIN town's in Brunswick,
By famous Hanover city;
　　The river Weser, deep and wide,
　　Washes its wall on the southern side;
　　A pleasanter spot you never spied;
But, when begins my ditty,
　　Almost five hundred years ago,
　　To see the townsfolk suffer so
　　　　From vermin, was a pity.

　　Rats!
They fought the dogs and killed the cats,
　　And bit the babies in the cradles,
And ate the cheeses out of the vats,
　　And licked the soup from the cooks' own ladles,
Split open the kegs of salted sprats,
Made nests inside men's Sunday hats,
And even spoiled the women's chats,
　　　　By drowning their speaking
　　　　With shrieking and squeaking
In fifty different sharps and flats.

At last the people in a body
 To the Town Hall came flocking:
' 'Tis clear,' cried they, 'our Mayor's a noddy;
 And as for our Corporation—shocking
To think we buy gowns lined with ermine
For dolts that can't or won't determine
What's best to rid us of our vermin!
You hope, because you're old and obese,
To find in the furry civic robe ease?
Rouse up, Sirs! Give your brains a racking
To find the remedy we're lacking,
Or, sure as fate, we'll send you packing!'
At this the Mayor and Corporation
Quaked with a mighty consternation.

An hour they sate in council,
 At length the Mayor broke silence;
'For a guilder I'd my ermine gown sell;
 I wish I were a mile hence!
It's easy to bid one rack one's brain—
I'm sure my poor head aches again
I've scratched it so, and all in vain.
Oh for a trap, a trap, a trap!'
Just as he said this, what should hap
At the chamber door but a gentle tap?
'Bless us,' cried the Mayor, 'what's that?'
(With the Corporation as he sat,
Looking little though wondrous fat;
Nor brighter was his eye, nor moister
Than a too-long-opened oyster,
Save when at noon his paunch grew mutinous
For a plate of turtle green and glutinous)

'Only a scraping of shoes on the mat?
Anything like the sound of a rat
Makes my heart go pit-a-pat!'

'Come in!'—the Mayor cried, looking bigger:
And in did come the strangest figure!
His queer long coat from heel to head
Was half of yellow and half of red;
And he himself was tall and thin,
With sharp blue eyes, each like a pin,
And light loose hair, yet swarthy skin,
No tuft on cheek nor beard on chin,
But lips where smiles went out and in—
There was no guessing his kith and kin!
And nobody could enough admire
The tall man and his quaint attire:
Quoth one: 'It's as my great-grandsire,
Starting up at the Trump of Doom's tone,
Had walked this way from his painted tombstone!'

He advanced to the council-table:
And 'Please your honours,' said he, 'I'm able,
By means of a secret charm to draw
All creatures living beneath the sun,
That creep or swim or fly or run,
After me so as you never saw!
And I chiefly use my charm
On creatures that do people harm,
The mole and toad and newt and viper;
And people call me the Pied Piper.'
(And here they noticed round his neck
A scarf of red and yellow stripe,
To match with his coat of the self-same check;
And at the scarf's end hung a pipe;
And his fingers, they noticed, were ever straying
As if impatient to be playing
Upon this pipe, as low it dangled
Over his vesture so old-fangled.)
'Yet,' said he, 'poor piper as I am,
In Tartary I freed the Cham,
Last June, from his huge swarms of gnats;
I eased in Asia the Nizam
Of a monstrous brood of vampire-bats:
And as for what your brain bewilders,
If I can rid your town of rats
Will you give me a thousand guilders?'
'One? fifty thousand!'—was the exclamation
Of the astonished Mayor and Corporation.

Into the street the Piper stept,
   Smiling first a little smile,
As if he knew what magic slept
   In his quiet pipe the while;
Then, like a musical adept,
To blow the pipe his lips he wrinkled,
And green and blue his sharp eyes twinkled
Like a candle-flame where salt is sprinkled;
And ere three shrill notes the pipe uttered,
You heard as if an army muttered;
And the muttering grew to a grumbling;
And the grumbling grew to a mighty rumbling;
And out of the houses the rats came tumbling.
Great rats, small rats, lean rats, brawny rats,
Brown rats, black rats, grey rats, tawny rats,
Grave old plodders, gay young friskers,
   Fathers, mothers, uncles, cousins,
Cocking tails and pricking whiskers,
   Families by tens and dozens,
Brothers, sisters, husbands, wives—
Followed the Piper for their lives.

From street to street he piped advancing,
And step for step they followed dancing,
Until they came to the river Weser
Wherein all plunged and perished!
—Save one who, stout as Julius Caesar,
Swam across and lived to carry
(As he, the manuscript he cherished)
To Rat-land home his commentary:
Which was, 'At the first shrill notes of the pipe,
I heard a sound as of scraping tripe,
And putting apples, wondrous ripe,
Into a cider-press's gripe:
And a moving away of pickle-tub-boards,
And a leaving ajar of conserve-cupboards,
And a drawing the corks of train-oil-flasks,
And a breaking the hoops of butter-casks;
And it seemed as if a voice
(Sweeter far than by harp or by psaltery
Is breathed) called out, 'Oh rats, rejoice!
The world is grown to one vast dry-saltery!
So, munch on, crunch on, take your nuncheon,
Breakfast, supper, dinner, luncheon!
And just as a bulky sugar-puncheon,
All ready staved, like a great sun shone
Glorious scarce an inch before me,
Just as methought it said, Come, bore me!
—I found the Weser rolling o'er me.'

You should have heard the Hamelin people
Ringing the bells till they rocked the steeple.
'Go,' cried the Mayor, 'and get long poles!
Poke out the nests and block up the holes!
Consult with carpenters and builders,
And leave in our town not even a trace
Of the rats!'—when suddenly, up the face
Of the Piper perked in the market-place,
With a, 'First, if you please, my thousand guilders!'

A thousand guilders! the Mayor looked blue;
So did the Corporation too.
For council dinners made rare havoc
With Claret, Moselle, Vin-de-Grave, Hock;
And half the money would replenish
Their cellar's biggest butt with Rhenish.
To pay this sum to a wandering fellow
With a gipsy coat of red and yellow!
'Beside,' quoth the Mayor with a knowing wink,
'Our business was done at the river's brink;
We saw with our eyes the vermin sink,
And what's dead can't come to life, I think.
So, friend, we're not the folks to shrink
From the duty of giving you something for drink,
And a matter of money to put in your poke;
But as for the guilders, what we spoke
Of them, as you very well know, was in joke.
Beside, our losses have made us thrifty.
A thousand guilders! Come, take fifty!'

The Piper's face fell, and he cried,
'No trifling! I can't wait, beside!
I've promised to visit by dinner-time
Bagdat, and accept the prime
Of the Head-Cook's pottage, all he's rich in,
For having left, in the Caliph's kitchen,
Of a nest of scorpions no survivor—
With him I proved no bargain-driver,
With you, don't think I'll bate a stiver!
And folks who put me in a passion
May find me pipe to another fashion.'

'How!' cried the Mayor, 'd'ye think I'll brook
Being worse treated than a Cook?
Insulted by a lazy ribald
With idle pipe and vesture piebald?
You threaten us, fellow? Do your worst,
Blow your pipe there till you burst!"

Once more he stept into the street;
   And to his lips again
Laid his long pipe of smooth straight cane;
   And ere he blew three notes (such sweet
Soft notes as yet musician's cunning
   Never gave the enraptured air)
There was a rustling, that seemed like a bustling
Of merry crowds justling at pitching and hustling,
Small feet were pattering, wooden shoes clattering,
Little hands clapping and little tongues chattering,
And, like fowls in a farm-yard when barley is scattering,
Out came the children running.

All the little boys and girls
With rosy cheeks and flaxen curls,
And sparkling eyes and teeth like pearls,
Tripping and skipping, ran merrily after
The wonderful music with shouting and laughter.

The Mayor was dumb, and the Council stood
As if they were changed into blocks of wood,
Unable to move a step, or cry
To the children merrily skipping by—
And could only follow with the eye
That joyous crowd at the Piper's back.
But how the Mayor was on the rack,
And the wretched Council's bosoms beat,
As the Piper turned from the High Street
To where the Weser rolled its waters
Right in the way of their sons and daughters!
However he turned from South to West,
And to Koppelberg Hill his steps addressed,
And after him the children pressed;
Great was the joy in every breast.
'He never can cross that mighty top!
He's forced to let the piping drop,
And we shall see our children stop!'
When, lo, as they reached the mountain's side,
A wondrous portal opened wide,
As if a cavern was suddenly hollowed;
And the Piper advanced and the children followed,
And when all were in to the very last,
The door in the mountain-side shut fast.
Did I say all? No! one was lame,
And could not dance the whole of the way;

And in after years, if you would blame
His sadness, he was used to say,—
'It's dull in our town since my playmates left!
I can't forget that I'm bereft
Of all the pleasant sights they see,
Which the Piper also promised me.
For he led us, he said, to a joyous land,
Joining the town and just at hand,
Where waters gushed and the fruit-trees grew,
And flowers put forth a fairer hue,
And everything was strange and new;
The sparrows were brighter than peacocks here,
And their dogs outran our fallow deer,
And honey-bees had lost their stings,
And horses were born with eagles' wings:
And just as I became assured
My lame foot would be speedily cured,
The music stopped and I stood still,
And found myself outside the Hill,
Left alone against my will,
To go now limping as before,
And never hear of that country more!'

Alas! alas for Hamelin!
    There came into many a burgher's pate
    A text which says, that Heaven's Gate
    Opes to the Rich at as easy rate
As the needle's eye takes a camel in!
The Mayor sent East, West, North and South,
To offer the Piper, by word of mouth,
    Wherever it was men's lot to find him,
Silver and gold to his heart's content,

THE PIED PIPER

from an etching by Jane Cook (about 1870)

If he'd only return the way he went,
   And bring the children after him.
But when they saw 'twas a lost endeavour,
And Piper and dancers were gone for ever,
They made a decree that lawyers never
   Should think their records dated duly
If, after the day of the month and year,
These words did not as well appear,
'And so long after what happened here
   On the Twenty-second of July,
Thirteen hundred and seventy-six:'
And the better in memory to fix
The place of the children's last retreat,
They called it, the Pied Piper's Street—
Where anyone playing on pipe or tabor
Was sure for the future to lose his labour.
Nor suffered they hostelry or tavern
   To shock with mirth a street so solemn;
But opposite the place of the cavern
   They wrote the story on a column,
And on the great Church-Window painted
The same, to make the world acquainted
How their children were stolen away;
And there it stands to this very day.
And I must not omit to say
That in Transylvania there's a tribe
Of alien people that ascribe
The outlandish ways and dress
On which their neighbours lay such stress,
To their fathers and mothers having risen
Out of some subterraneous prison
Into which they were trepanned
Long time ago in a mighty band

Out of Hamelin town in Brunswick land,
But how or why, they don't understand.

So, Willy, let you and me be wipers
Of scores out with all men—especially pipers:
And, whether they pipe us free, from rats or from mice,
If we've promised them aught, let us keep our promise.

ROBERT BROWNING

INDEX OF TITLES AND FIRST LINES

Titles are given in italic type

When icicles hang by the wall 8
Where the bee sucks, there suck I 52
Where thou dwellest, in what grove 9
Wind and waters ring the bells 10
Witch Stepmother, The 85
Woe's me, woe's me 33
Written in March 3

'You are old, Father William,' the young man said 99
York, York for my Money 54

INDEX OF AUTHORS